Conten

CW00970931

Squirrel

He flies without wings.
He jumps without springs.
High in the treetops
he chatters and sings:

racing,

chasing,

squirrel.

He tiptoes on branches.
He takes lots of chances.
His tail helps him balance
Wherever he dances:

jumping,

bumping,

squirrel.

He shakes the nuts down
when they're shiny and brown.
He nibbles them, dropping
their shells on the ground:

cracking,

snacking,

squirrel.

Celia Warren

Who took the cake?

Look what Mum found when she was working
in the garden one morning!

"Who put these here?" she asked the children.

"Not us," they said. "But we know where they
come from."

"Where?" asked Mum.

"Up that big tree there," they said.

They ran off to play and Mum went on working in the garden. When she looked under some logs, she had another surprise.

"What's this?" she said.

Then she called to the children.

"Come here, please," she shouted,

and they came running down the garden.

"Did you put these here?" Mum asked.

"No, we didn't," said the children.

"And we don't know who did."

"I can't think who hid these things in my garden," she said. "Let's go and ask Dan."

"I didn't see who did it," said Dan.

"I have just come back from the supermarket."

"Oh, Dan!" said the children. "What a big cake!
Can we have some?"

"Yes, you can," said Dan.

"And I'll make some tea," said Mum.

When they were having their tea and cake,
the snow came down ... over the house, over
the trees, and over the garden.
The children looked out.
"Can we take some cake for our little friends?"
they asked. "They will need some food now
the snow has come."

"Yes," said Mum. "But come back when
you have put the cake out."

So the children went into the garden with
the cake. When they came in, the children
helped to put away the shopping and the
tea things.

Then they went to look out at the snow.

And what a surprise they had.

They saw that there was no cake and

no bread out in the garden.

"Did they eat all that cake so soon?"

the children asked.

"I don't think so," said Mum.

"They don't eat as fast as that."

"Then who did?"

"Let's go and find out who took it," said Mum.
They all went into the garden ... and
they saw some tracks in the snow.

"I think these tracks were made by the animal who took the cake," said Dan.

"And I think it was that animal who put things under the logs," said Mum.

"Let's follow the tracks and find him."

Soon they came to a big tree at the end of
the garden.

"Let's look in here," said Mum.

"I'll help you up so that you can see."

"It's a squirrel," shouted the children.

"Shh!" said Mum. "He is asleep. Let him be."

"Now we know who took the cake, Mum,"
said the children.

"Yes, the squirrel did," said Mum, " ... and
now we'll look after him, too."

Elephants

If a hundred elephants
tried to board a bus
would the driver
make a fuss?

And if fifty elephants
came all together
to do their shopping at Tesco
would there be a fiasco?

And if twenty elephants
came to school
one morning
with books in their trunks
would the teacher
keep her cool?

And if one
very little elephant
smaller than all the rest
wanted to be my friend
for just one day
would my mum
let him stay?

Irene Rawnsley

A holiday in India

"When I was a boy," said Dad,
"this was my home."

"It was my home, too," said Mum.
"We know you will like it here."

"Are there lots of animals to see?" asked Ashi.

"Yes," said Dad. "Come on.
We'll go and look at some now."

So they went down the track and into the trees.

"What's that big animal over there?" asked Ashi.

"It's an elephant," said Mum.

"Does she live here?" asked Ashi.

"Oh yes," said Dad. "This morning she's working with that man. She's helping him with the trees."

There was another elephant down the track.
"What's she doing?"

"She's going to put the logs into the river,"
said Dad.

"Let's follow her and see how she does it,"
said Ashi. "Can we ... please, Mum?"

"You go with Dad," said Mum, "and I'll follow."

So Dad and Ashi went after the elephant.
"Just look at the tracks she makes," said Dad.

"Look at the tracks we make," laughed Ashi.
"When Mum comes, I think she will follow our
tracks. Then she will know where we are."

When they got down to the river, they found
the big elephant helping to put the logs in the
water. There was another elephant there, too.
But this was a baby elephant.

"He's having fun in the water," said Ashi.

"Please can I go and play with him?"

But just then Mum came. "Come on, you two,"
she called. "We'll have to go back now."

As they went back, Ashi looked down ... and
there was another animal track.
She didn't know what animal had made this one,
but she wanted to find out.
She didn't say a thing to her mum and dad,
she just ran off.

She didn't know that a snake had made that
track ... and that the snake was hiding
in the grass.

"Where are you going?" Mum called out.

"Come back, Ashi."

But Ashi went running off, and soon she came
to where the snake was hiding ...
Danger! Danger!
"Stop where you are, Ashi," shouted Dad.
"We'll get help."

Just as Dad was about to run and get help ...
help came.

One of the big elephants took Ashi, and
put her up on her back so that Ashi was
out of danger from the snake.

"Elephants can do lots of things,
can't they, Dad?" said Ashi.

"Lots of things," said Dad.

"Thank you for helping me," Ashi said to
the elephant.